Nature Sketch Journal

Drawing and Writing Pages and References for Budding Scientists

CLASSICALCONVERSATIONS.COM

Nature Sketch Journal: Drawing and Writing Pages and References for Budding Scientists

Created by Courtney Sanford and Jennifer Greenholt

Published in the U.S.A. by Classical Conversations, Inc.
P.O. Box 909
West End, NC 27376

ISBN: 978-0-9904720-4-9

For ordering information, visit www.ClassicalConversationsBooks.com.
Printed in the United States of America

Nature Sketch Journal
Drawing and Writing Pages and References
for Budding Scientists

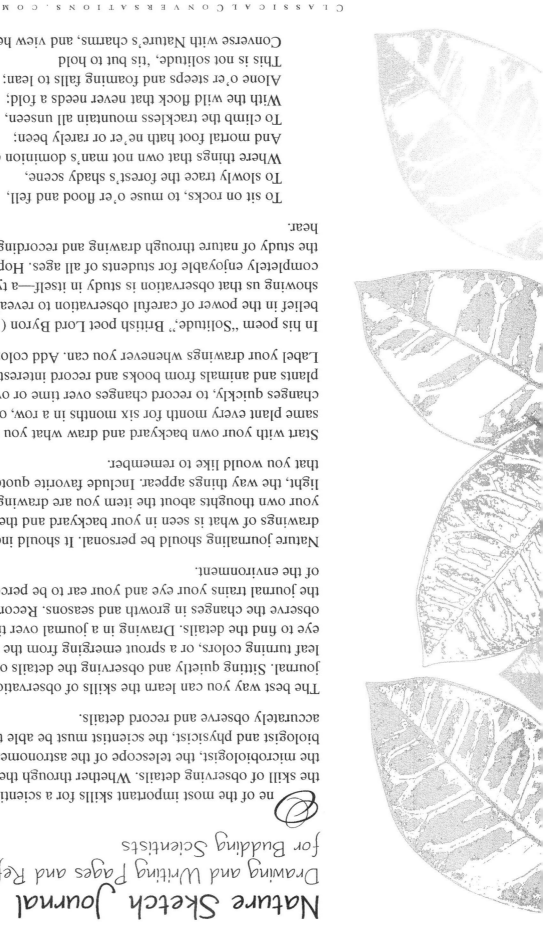

ne of the most important skills for a scientist to develop is the skill of observing details. Whether through the microscope of the microbiologist, the telescope of the astronomer, or the eye of the biologist and physicist, the scientist must be able to patiently and accurately observe and record details.

The best way you can learn the skills of observation is to keep a nature journal. Sitting quietly and observing the details of a fern unfolding, a leaf turning colors, or a sprout emerging from the soil will train your eye to find the details. Drawing in a journal over time trains your eye to observe the changes in growth and seasons. Recording detailed notes in the journal trains your eye and your ear to be perceptive of many details of the environment.

Nature journaling should be personal. It should include scientific drawings of what is seen in your backyard and the places you visit, plus your own thoughts about the item you are drawing, and the season, the light, the way things appear. Include favorite quotes or poems or sayings that you would like to remember.

Start with your own backyard and draw what you see there. Draw the same plant every month for six months in a row, or every week if it changes quickly, to record changes over time or over the seasons. Draw plants and animals from books and record interesting facts about them. Label your drawings wherever you can. Add color with colored pencils.

In his poem "Solitude," British poet Lord Byron (1788–1824) shows his belief in the power of careful observation to reveal the secrets of nature, showing us that observation is study in itself—a type of study that is completely enjoyable for students of all ages. Hopefully you will enjoy the study of nature through drawing and recording what you see and hear.

> To sit on rocks, to muse o'er flood and fell,
> To slowly trace the forest's shady scene,
> Where things that own not man's dominion dwell,
> And mortal foot hath ne'er or rarely been;
> To climb the trackless mountain all unseen,
> With the wild flock that never needs a fold;
> Alone o'er steeps and foaming falls to lean;
> This is not solitude, 'tis but to hold
> Converse with Nature's charms, and view her stores unrolled.

Labeling a drawing helps students learn scientific vocabulary.

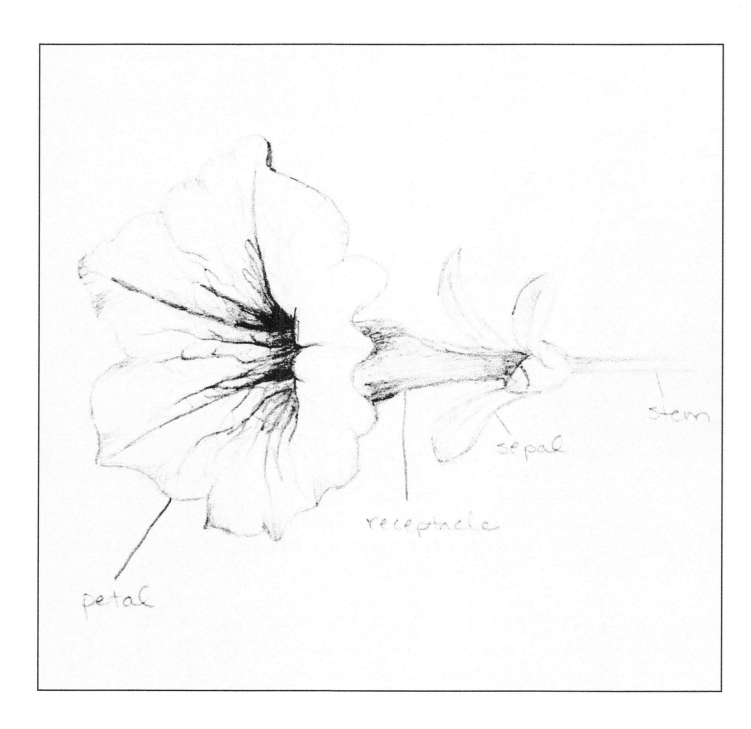

Drawing by Katerina Kern

There is a pleasure in the pathless

woods,

There is a rapture on the lonely shore,

There is society, where none intrudes,

By the deep sea, and music in its roar:

I love not man the less, but Nature more,

From these our interviews, in which I

steal

From all I may be, or have been before,

To mingle with the Universe, and feel

What I can ne'er express, yet cannot all

conceal.

—Lord Byron, "Childe Harold's Pilgrimage" (excerpt)

Student Work

With practice, students can progress from simple sketches to beautiful scientific drawings.

Drawings by Daniel Shirley (at age 12)

Drawings by Katerina Kern, post graduation

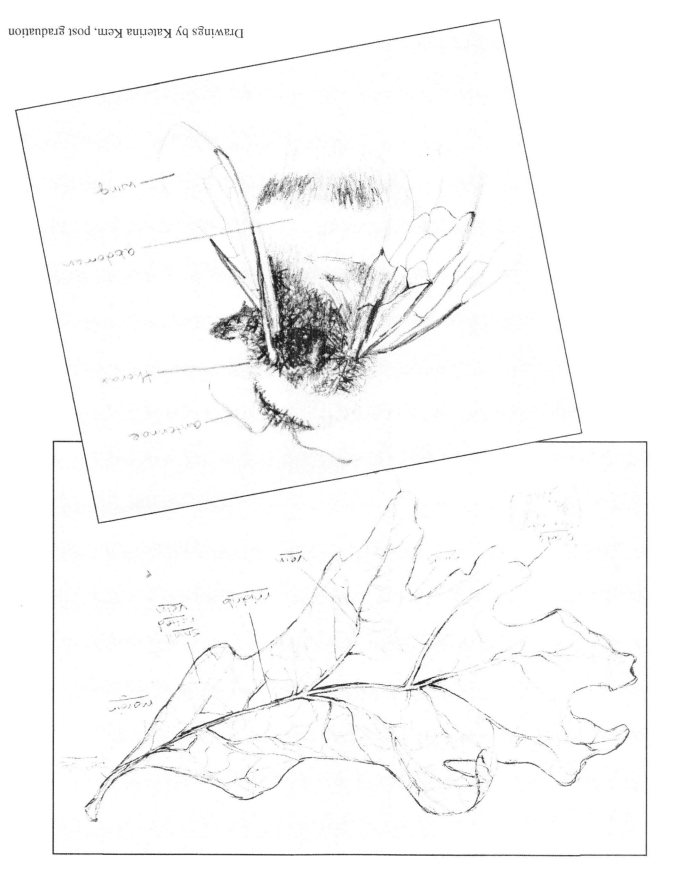

M74
MARS
CONSTALATION
ALL STARS PLACED ACURATLY AS OF AUG. 24TH
2H
EAST
CONSTALATION

ASTRONOMY

I HAVE BEEN OBSERERVING MARS

LIFE ON MARS "DAVID BOWIE" -SONG

MY FAVROITE MARS QUOTE RELATED TO MARS
"I WOULD LIKE TO DIE ON MARS, JUST NOT ON IMPACT..."-
ELON MUSK.

Shall man confine his Maker's sway
    To Gothic domes of mouldering stone?
Thy temple is the face of day;
    Earth, ocean, heaven thy boundless throne.
—Lord Byron, "The Prayer of Nature" (excerpt)

So will I build my altar in the fields,
And the blue sky my fretted dome shall be,
And the sweet fragrance that the wild flower yields
Shall be the incense I will yield to Thee,
Thee only God! and thou shalt not despise
Even me, the priest of this poor sacrifice.

—Samuel Coleridge, "To Nature" (excerpt)

HAPPY insect! what can be
In happiness compar'd to thee?
Fed with nourishment divine,
The dewy morning's gentle wine!

—Anacreon, "The Grasshopper" (excerpt)

All things bright and beautiful,
All creatures great and small,
All things wise and wonderful:
The Lord God made them all.

Each little flower that opens,
Each little bird that sings,
He made their glowing colors,
He made their tiny wings.

The purple-headed mountains,
The river running by,
The sunset and the morning
That brightens up the sky.

The cold wind in the winter,
The pleasant summer sun,
The ripe fruits in the garden,
He made them every one.

The tall trees in the greenwood,
The meadows where we play,
The rushes by the water,
To gather every day.

He gave us eyes to see them,
And lips that we might tell
How great is God Almighty,
Who has made all things well.

—Cecil Alexander, "All Things Bright
and Beautiful"

For ye shall go out with joy,
and be led forth with peace:
the mountains and the hills shall
break forth before you into
singing, and all the trees of the
field shall clap their hands.

—Isaiah 55:12 (KJV)

"Great things are done when
men and mountains meet."

—William Blake

"This curious world we
inhabit is more wonderful than
convenient; more beautiful
than it is useful; it is more to be
admired and enjoyed than used."

—Henry David Thoreau

God made a beauteous garden
With lovely flowers strown,
But one straight, narrow pathway
That was not overgrown.
And to this beauteous garden
He brought mankind to live,
And said: "To you, my children,
These lovely flowers I give.
Prune ye my vines and fig trees,
With care my flowerets tend,
But keep the pathway open
Your home is at the end.

—Robert Frost, "God's Garden" (excerpt)

You alone are the LORD;
You have made heaven,
The heaven of heavens, with all their host,
The earth and everything on it,
The seas and all that is in them,
And You preserve them all.
The host of heaven worships You.
—Nehemiah 9:6 (NKJV)

The budding twigs spread out their fan,
To catch the breezy air;
And I must think, do all I can,
That there was pleasure there.

—William Wordsworth,
"Lines Written in Early Spring" (excerpt)

"Nature does nothing uselessly."

—Aristotle, *Politics*

The flowers appear on the earth, the time of singing has come, and the voice of the turtledove is heard in our land. —Song of Solomon 2:12 (ESV)

Reference Section

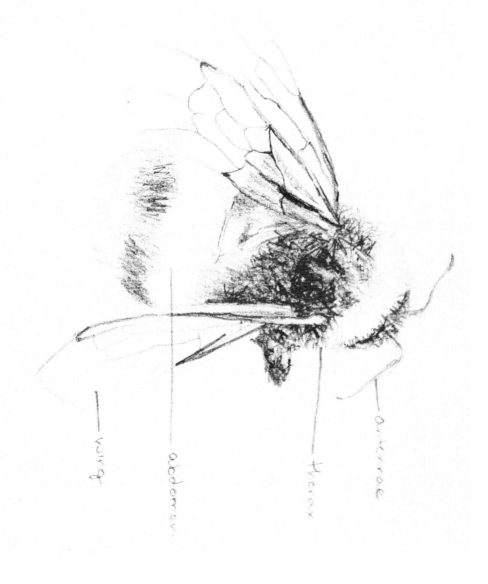

wing

abdomen

thorax

antennae

*But ask the beasts, and they will teach you; the birds of the heavens,
and they will tell you; or the bushes of the earth, and they will teach you;
and the fish of the sea will declare to you. Who among all these does not know
that the hand of the LORD has done this? In his hand is the life
of every living thing and the breath of all mankind.*

—Job 12:7–10 (ESV)

Drawing by Katerina Kern

Interesting Facts

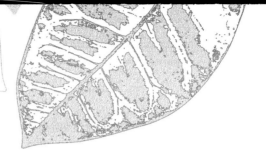

- The oldest tree alive is over 5,000 years old! It lives in California and is named Methuselah.

- A bee must take pollen from 4,000 flowers to produce one tablespoon of honey.

- Leaves always have orange, yellow, and red pigment called chlorophyl in them. You can't see them in the summer because the green chlorophyl covers them up. In the fall the leaves get rid of the green chlorophyl and the other colors become visible.

- Crickets can tell you the temperature outside. Just count the number of chirps in 15 seconds and add 37.

- All insects have six legs.

- Ants stretch their legs when they wake up in the morning.

- Foxgloves are pretty little flowers that look like bells. Their name comes from an old English myth that foxes slipped these flowers on their feet to sneak up on prey without being heard.

- Sunflowers move with the sun throughout the day to soak up all the sunlight they can.

- The largest flower in the world is called the *Rafflesia arnoldii*. It lives in the rainforest and can grow up to three feet wide. That's big enough for a child to sit inside!

LIVING THINGS

Living things are able to reproduce, move and grow, respond to a stimulus, and carry on metabolic activities.

MONERA — Simple cells, no nuclei; includes bacteria.

PROTISTA — Mostly single-celled; includes algae, amoebae, and protozoans.

FUNGI — Single- or multi-celled, have cell wall, absorb food, no chlorophyll, decomposers; includes molds, yeasts, mushrooms.

PLANTAE — Multi-cellular, produce own food through photosynthesis, have cell walls; includes seedless plants: ferns, horsetails, liverworts, mosses; and seed plants: monocots (herbs) and dicots (wildflowers), and some trees, and conifers (pine trees, fir trees).

ANIMALIA — Multi-cellular, mobile, obtain food by ingestion, no rigid cell walls.

Mollusks — snail, slug, clam.

Arthropods — Arachnids: spider, scorpion, tick, horseshoe crab.
Insects: incomplete metamorphosis: fly, beetle, grasshopper, cockroach, dragonfly
complete metamorphosis: butterfly, moth, bee, wasp, ant.

Sponges

Stinging-cell animals

Flatworms

Roundworms

Segmented worms

Sea stars

Birds — Warm-blooded, feathered, lay eggs; includes owls, birds of prey.

Amphibians — Cold-blooded, smooth moist skin, jelly-like eggs, metamorphosis, live in water then on land; includes toad, frog, salamander.

Reptiles — Cold-blooded, tough scaly skin, lungs, soft leathery eggs laid on land; includes snake, lizard, tortoise, alligator, crocodile.

Fish — Cold-blooded, gills, fins, jelly-like eggs laid in water; includes jawless (lamprey), bony (tuna, trout, salmon, sardine), cartilaginous (shark, ray, skate).

Mammals — Warm-blooded, hair, live-birth. There are 21 orders of mammals and 4,000 different kinds. Some unusual mammals are: **Marsupials,** who carry their young in a pouch: kangaroo, koala, wombat, opossum. **Bats,** who are flying mammals; there are nearly 1,000 species. **Marine Mammals,** who live in the sea: killer whales, toothed whales, baleen whales, sperm whales, dolphin, porpoise, narwhal. **Humans,** who walk on two feet, talking, tool-using, clothing-wearing mammals.

For more information:
Classical Acts & Facts® Science Cards–
Biology and Geology

Scientific Method

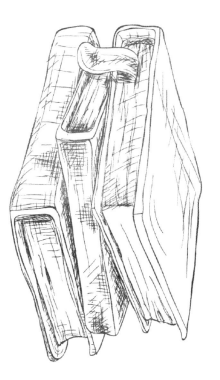

Observe:
Observe or read about a phenomenon.

Hypothesize:
Wonder about your observations and invent a hypothesis—a "guess"—that could explain the phenomenon or set of facts that you have observed.

Predict:
Use the logical consequences of your hypothesis to predict observations of new phenomena or results of new measurements.

Verify:
Perform experiments to test these predictions, to find just which prediction occurred.

Evaluate:
Search for other possible explanations of the result until you can show, with confidence, that your guess was indeed the explanation.

Publish:
Tell others of your results. Other scientists can then review your reasoning and see if they can also repeat the result. This is known as peer review.

Timeline
of Famous Scientists

HIPPOCRATES began the study of medicine.

ARCHIMEDES invented the sciences of mechanics and hydrostatics and discovered the laws of levers and pulleys.

HIPPARCHUS cataloged the stars.

PTOLEMY formed the geocentric theory of the solar system.

LEONARDO DA VINCI developed scientific study through observation (similar to Scientific Method).

COPERNICUS formed the heliocentric view of the solar system.

"Finally I give this advice to any people who might be completely unfamiliar with mathematical questions... If such readers were to be terrified by the difficulty of the geometrical argument, they might deprive themselves of the most joyful fruit of contemplating the harmonies. Now, let us go to work with God." —Kepler

GALILEO GALILEI invented the telescope.

JOHANNES KEPLER formulated three laws of planetary motion.

"[When] I study the book of nature, I find myself oftentimes reduced to exclaim with the Psalmist, How manifold are Thy works, O Lord! in wisdom hast Thou made them all!" —Boyle

BLAISE PASCAL invented the calculator.

ROBERT BOYLE launched the field of chemistry.

ISAAC NEWTON developed laws of universal gravitation and motion.

"Let man then contemplate the whole of nature in her full and grand majesty; and turn his vision from the low objects which surround him. Let him gaze on that brilliant light, set like an eternal lamp to illumine the universe... In short, it is the greatest sensible mark of the almighty power of God, that imagination loses itself in that thought." —Pascal

"Whence is it that Nature doth nothing in vain; and whence arises all that Order and Beauty which we see in the World? ... does it not appear from Phaenomena that there is a Being incorporeal, living, intelligent, omnipresent..." —Newton

DANIEL BERNOULLI developed principles of the flow of fluids.

CARL LINNAEUS developed the precursor to the modern classification system of living things.

"...[man] is noble in his nature, in as much as, by the powers of his mind, he is able to reason justly upon whatever discovers itself to his senses; and to look with reverence and wonder, upon the works of Him who created all things....It is therefore the business of a thinking being, to look forward to the purposes of all things; and to remember that the end of creation is, that God may be glorified in all his works." —Linnaeus

400 BC

287 BC

100 BC

1 AD

1400

1500

1600

1700

MICHAEL FARADAY invented the electric motor.

"Shall we educate ourselves in what is known, and then casting away all we have acquired, turn to our ignorance for aid, and to guide us among the unknown? If so, instinct is more to write, but employ one who is unacquainted with letters to read that which is written; the end will be just as unsatisfactory, though not so important; for the book of nature, which we have to read, is written by the finger of God." ("On Mental Education" lecture, 1854)

GREGOR MENDEL formalized the study of genetics.

"So natural and supernatural must unite in the realization of the Holiness to the people. Man must contribute his minimum work of toil, and God gives the growth. Truly, the seed, the talent, the grace of God is there, and man has simply to work, take the seeds to bring them to the bankers. So that we 'may have life, and abundantly.'" ("Sermon on Easter," c. 1867)

JAMES CLERK MAXWELL discovered the relationship between electricity and magnetism.

...I have the capacity of being more wicked than any example that man could set me, and... if I escape, it is only by God's grace helping me to get rid of myself partially in science... but not perfectly except by committing myself to God." (Letter to Rev. C. B. Tayler)

THOMAS EDISON invented the light bulb, phonograph, and motion picture camera.

JOSEPH LISTER developed antiseptic surgery.

MAX PLANCK originated quantum theory.

"Both religion and natural science require a belief in God for their activities, to the former He is the starting point, to the latter the goal of every thought process. To the former He is the foundation, to the latter, the crown of the edifice of every generalized world view." ("Religion and Natural Science," lecture 1937)

ALBERT EINSTEIN developed the theory of relativity.

NEILS BOHR developed the Bohr model of the atom.

EDWIN HUBBLE discovered galaxies beyond the Milky Way.

JAMES WATSON & FRANCIS CRICK published the structure of the DNA molecule.

SAMUEL MORSE invented the telegraph and Morse code.

CHARLES DARWIN popularized the theory of natural selection and the theory of evolution.

CHARLES BABBAGE invented a calculating engine and became the father of computing.

"Almost all thinking men who have studied the laws which govern the animate and the inanimate world around us, agree that the belief in the existence of one Supreme Creator, possessed of infinite wisdom and power, is open to far less difficulties than the supposition of the absence of any cause, or the existence of a plurality of causes." (Passages from the Life of a Philosopher)

LOUIS PASTEUR confirmed the germ theory of disease and developed pasteurization.

"Absolute faith in God and in Eternity, and a conviction that the power for good given to us in this world will be continued beyond it, with feelings which pervaded his whole life." (Vallery-Radot [son-in-law] The Life of Pasteur, 1911)

LORD KELVIN developed an absolute temperature scale and formulated the second law of thermodynamics.

"But overpoweringly strong proofs of intelligent and benevolent design lie all round us, and if ever perplexities, whether metaphysical or scientific, turn us away from them for a time, they come back upon us with irresistible force, showing to us through nature the influence of a free will, and teaching us that all living beings depend on one ever-acting Creator and Ruler." (Presidential Address to the British Association for the Advancement of Science, 1871)

MARIE CURIE discovered polonium and radium.

GEORGE WASHINGTON CARVER used chemistry to improve agricultural production in the American South.

"How I thank God every day that I can walk and talk with majesty and power through a little specimen of mineral sent me for analysis from Bakersfield, California. I have dissolved it, purified it, made conditions favorable for the formation of crystals, when lo before my very eyes, a beautiful bunch of sea green crystals have formed and alongside of them a bunch of snow white ones. Marvel of marvels, how I wish I had you in God's little workshop for a while, how your soul would be thrilled and lifted up." (1927 letter to YMCA official Jack Boyd)

Measurements

Quantity	Base Unit - Metric	Base Unit - English
Mass	gram (g)	slug (sl)
Distance	meter (m)	foot (ft)
Volume	liter (L)	gallon (g)
Time	seconds (s)	second (s)
Temperature	Celsius (C)	Fahrenheit (F)
Electric current	ampere (A)	ampere (A)
Amt. of matter	mole (mol)	mole (mol)

Prefix (Symbol)	Numerical Meaning
tera- (T)	10^{12} = 1,000,000,000,000
giga- (G)	10^{9} = 1,000,000,000
mega- (M)	10^{6} = 1,000,000
kilo (k)	10^{3} = 1,000
hecto- (h)	10^{2} = 100
deca- (da)	10 = 10
deci- (d)	10^{-1} = 0.1
centi- (c)	10^{-2} = 0.01
milli- (m)	10^{-3} = 0.001
micro- (μ)	10^{-6} = 0.000001
nano- (n)	10^{-9} = 0.000000001

Converting Between U.S. Customary Units

Length:

1 inch = 1/12 foot
1 foot = 12 inches or 1/3 yard
1 yard = 36 inches or 3 feet
1 mile = 5,280 feet or 1,760 yards

Liquid Volume or Capacity:

1 fluid ounce = 1/16 pint
1 pint = 16 fluid ounces or 2 cups
1 quart = 2 pints or 1/4 gallon
1 gallon = 4 quarts or 8 pints or 16 cups

Weight:

1 pound = 16 ounces
1 ton = 2,000 pounds

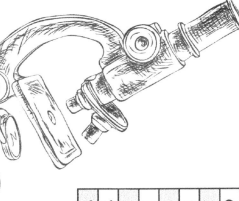

Converting from U.S. Customary Units to Metric Units

1 inch = 2.54 centimeters

1 inch = 25.4 millimeters

1 foot = 30.48 centimeters

1 yard = 0.91 meters

1 mile = 1.61 kilometers

1 fluid ounce = 29.57 milliliters

1 pint = 0.47 liters

1 quart = 0.95 liters

1 gallon = 3.79 liters

1 ounce = 28.35 grams

1 pound = 0.45 kilograms

Converting Between Celsius and Fahrenheit

$F = (C \times 9/5) + 32$

$C = (F - 32) \times 5/9$

Boiling Point of Water	212°F	100°C
Normal Body Temperature	98.6°F	37°C
Freezing Point of Water	32°F	0°C

Parts per million (ppm): The number of molecules (or atoms) of a substance in a mixture for every 1 million molecules (or atoms) in that mixture (1% = 10,000 ppm)

Conversion Factors Commonly Used in Chemistry

1 slug = 14.59 kg

1 amu = 1.66 x 10⁻²⁴ g

1 atm = 101.3 kPa

1 calorie = 4.184 joules

1 food calorie (Cal) = 1,000 chemistry calories (cal)

760 torr = 1 atm

760 mm Hg = 1 atm

Periodic Table of the Elements

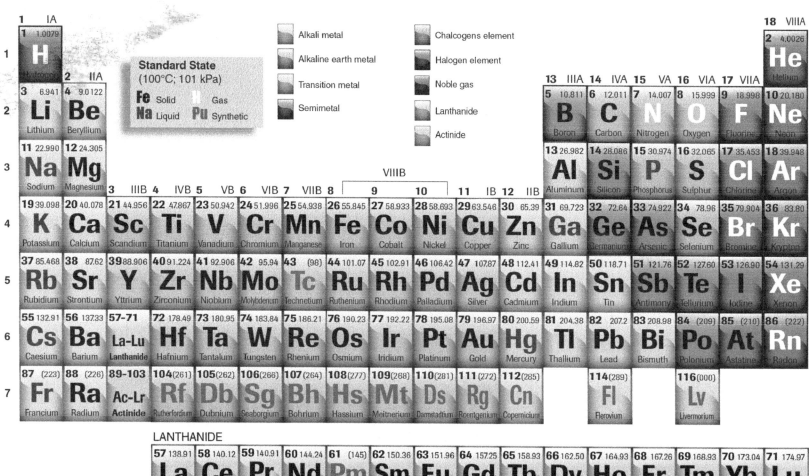

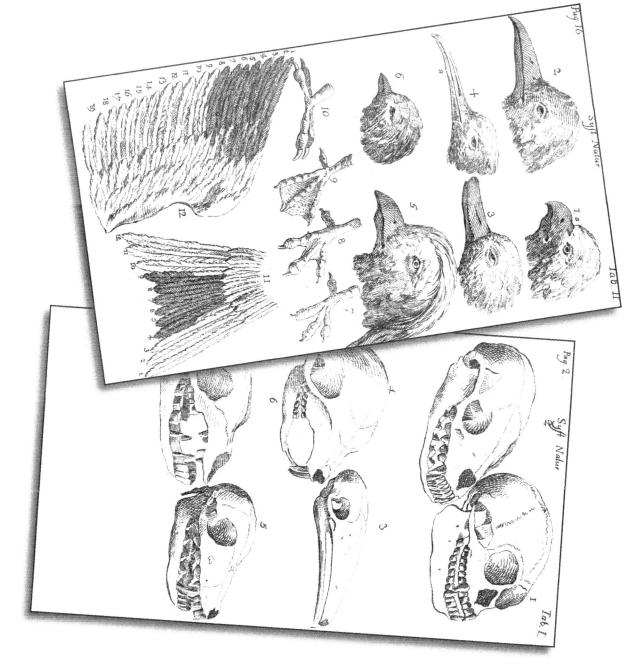

SYSTEMA NATURÆ

CAROLI LINNÆI

Naturæ Curioforum *Dioscoridis* Secundi

Famous Sketchbooks

Classical Acts & Facts® Science Cards

Classical Acts & Facts® Science Cards put science right at your fingertips! Marie Curie once said, "I am among those who think that science has great beauty." With the beautiful images and artwork that accompany each clearly-explained science fact, you will come to believe in the beauty of science, too. The high-quality, laminated 5" x 8" cards are arranged into four sets according to major science categories. This exclusive series of science cards is designed to serve you throughout your educational journey, with a comprehensive set of grammar pegs that relate to Foundations memory work all the way through the Challenge program's sciences. Over 120 unique acts and facts in all!

Biology and Geology
Ecology, Astronomy, Physics
Anatomy, Chemistry, Origins
Famous Scientists and More

Science Lab Journal

Develop strong observation and data recording skills with this rich, beautiful lab notebook. This lab book is used during actual labs to record procedures, collect data, and draw observations. Students have lined pages for recording lab procedures and observations and quadrille-ruled pages for recording data, making charts, and creating drawings. A reference section in the back makes it easy to double-check unit conversions as needed or check commonly used formulas. Also included is a timeline of famous scientists, the periodic table, the scientific method chart, and more. A ruler on the back cover makes it easy to be accurate during labs.

Discovering Atomos

This booklet is designed to give 6th–8th graders a basic introduction to chemical processes at the atomic level. The text is divided into six simple lessons that introduce various topics and then provide examples and exercises to support the new concepts. *Discovering Atomos* is a consumable workbook. Allowing students to write directly in the manual makes it easy for them to look back at helpful charts and figures, compare their work to the examples given, and reference the information that they have learned. The lessons in the text are meant to create a foundation for further studies in chemistry. If students can memorize the periodic table and learn how to combine elements now, higher level chemistry will be less intimidating right from the start. If students can learn that understanding chemistry is feasible and even fun, their success in the subject will already be well on its way. *Atomos* is a Greek word from which the word "atom" is derived. *Atomos* means "indivisible" (*a* means "not"; *temnein* means "to cut").